The New Christmas Activity Book

Written by Susan Vesey

Illustrated by Paul Granger

A LION BOOK

Oxford · Batavia · Sydney

The New Christmas Activity Book is full of good things — it is a book to enjoy. Here are some of the reasons why:

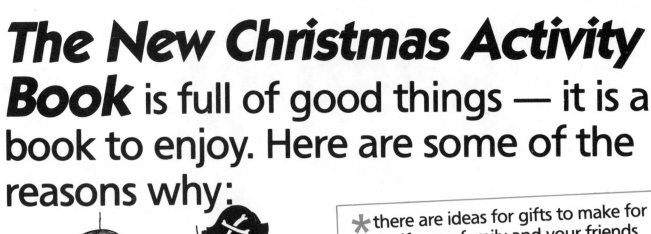

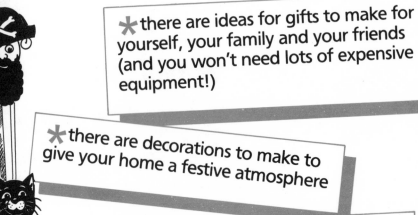

✱ there are ideas for gifts to make for yourself, your family and your friends (and you won't need lots of expensive equipment!)

✱ there are decorations to make to give your home a festive atmosphere

✱ there are novelty Christmas cards to make with peep-through cut-outs and stained glass windows

✱ there are games to give all the family lots of fun

✱ there is a fantastic theatre to make and use

✱ there are puzzles and quizzes to fill all those spare moments

✱ there is an Advent Calendar to put together, to count-down the days to Christmas

Best of all, the story of Christmas is told in its pages.
We hope you enjoy every part of <u>The New Christmas Activity Book</u>. Merry Christmas to you!

Can you re-unite these pairs?

Answers on page 48.

Your puppet theatre

The puppet theatre is not something that can be made in a few minutes: take plenty of time and a little care and you will have a theatre of which to be proud — something that will give you hours of pleasure.

Rather than print a script, the Christmas story is told throughout the book. Once you know the story well you can rehearse your own words and movements.

Perhaps you could start a family tradition on Christmas Eve by telling the Christmas story using your puppet theatre.

Hints for the play

Read the Christmas story so you know what happens and in what order. Think about how the various people must have felt and how they might have reacted. Fill in the speech bubbles to practise what the characters might say. Rehearse each scene until you feel happy with what you are doing.

A couple of torches can create some interesting lighting effects. No doubt you will work out how to produce the sound effects!

4

The first Christmas

The first Christmas happened nearly two thousand years ago when a baby called Jesus was born. Ever since then, people all around the world have celebrated Jesus' birthday. It all began like this...

There was a girl named Mary who lived in the town of Nazareth, in the country we now call Israel. She was an ordinary girl, from an ordinary family. When Mary was old enough, her parents arranged for her to be married. This was the custom. And so she was engaged to Joseph, the local carpenter.

One day, while Mary was at home by herself, a stranger appeared, as if from nowhere.

'God be with you!' he said, as he greeted her. 'You have been chosen for a very special purpose.'

The stranger was no ordinary person but one of God's angels. Mary loved God, but she was frightened by this greeting. She did not know what to think.

'Don't be afraid,' said the angel. 'I have come to tell you that you are going to have a baby – the Son of God himself. He will be called Jesus. He will be a King, like his ancestor King David, but his kingdom will never end.'

Mary was astonished.

'But I'm not married yet,' she protested. 'It isn't possible.'

'Nothing is impossible with God,' the angel replied. 'Your cousin Elizabeth thought she could never have a child. But now she is expecting a baby. God simply asks you to trust him.'

At once, Mary knew that it was true. This was a message from God. Her heart was full of wonder and joy.

'I will do whatever God wants,' she said.

Merry Christmas!

Can you match the words to the language? Answers on page 48.

Nadolig Llawen	Swedish
God Jul	Gaelic
Joyeux Noël	Italian
Feliz Navidad	French
Frohe Weihnachten	Welsh
Buon Natale	Dutch
Vrolyk Kerstfeest	Spanish
Nollag Shona Dhuit	German

Advent gift calendar

This idea needs quite a lot of planning, but it is a super gift to make for a younger brother or sister.

You will need:

- 25 small boxes — matchboxes or the boxes that hold photographic film
- 25 small gifts — see below for suggestions
- 25 pieces of paper small enough to tuck into your boxes
- reel of coloured thread

1
Glue or sticky tape the boxes together. Decorate the outside and mark the lids or flaps of the boxes from 1 to 25.

2
Write one verse of the Christmas story onto each piece of paper. Roll up into a mini-scroll and tie the thread round it.

3
Put a mini-scroll and a tiny gift into each box and close them so there is no peeping!

Gift suggestions for your Advent boxes

December 1 wrapped toffee
December 2 eraser
December 3 badge
December 4 puzzle
December 5 coin
December 6 wrapped chocolate
December 7 bookmark
December 8 unshelled peanut
December 9 bathcube
December 10 balloon
December 11 wrapped mint
December 12 ribbon
December 13 marble
December 14 pressed flower
December 15 toy soldier
December 16 party hat
December 17 coin
December 18 toy farm animal
December 19 marble
December 20 balloon
December 21 raisins
December 22 coin
December 23 pencil sharpener
December 24 crystallized fruit
December 25 Merry Christmas!

Advent promises

If you do not want to put tiny gifts inside, why not put a promise in instead! This makes a good gift for your parents.

'Today i will clean all the shoes.'

'Today I will wash the dishes.'

'Today I will tidy my bedroom.'

'Today I will give you a hug.'

Did you know...

The word 'advent' comes from the Latin *ad vento* which means arrival. Advent begins on the fourth Sunday before Christmas when we look forward to celebrating the arrival of Jesus.

A host of angels

A host of silver Christmas angels looks delightful against a live Christmas tree, but you could also make them into a mobile with strong thread or string — or simply stand them on the window ledge.

1

Trace these lines onto the card to make the body and wings of the angels. Cut round the shapes. Use these card templates to mark and cut out the coloured foil.

2

Glue the pipe-cleaner into the neck of the bauble and fix a circle of tinsel around the top.

3

Staple D1 to D2.
Staple A2 to A3 to A1.
Staple wings on B and C.

4

Push the pipe-cleaner and bauble down into the neck of the angel to make the head.

D2

A3

D1

A1

B

C

A2

Did you know ?

The word angel comes from the Greek word that means messenger. Although we often see pictures of angels with wings and haloes, we read in the Bible that they often looked like ordinary people – but came with a special message from God.

To make the theatre

There is some measuring and marking to do first.

You will need:
- shoebox
- scissors
- pencil
- ruler
- old Christmas cards
- glue

1

Mark two thick lines on the long side of the shoebox, about 10mm from the back and about 15mm apart.

2

Repeat this on the two sides, starting about 15mm from the back. The lines must go right to the floor, but not to the top.

3

Ask an adult to cut out slits ½mm wide where you have made the marks. This is difficult to do neatly with scissors. Encourage him or her to use a cutting knife if there is one available.

4

Paint the inside of the stage black and decorate the outside with pictures taken from old Christmas cards, or wrapping paper. Don't throw away the backs of the Christmas cards — you will need them later!

To make the scenery for your theatre, turn to pages 12, 16, 20, 28, 32 and 36.

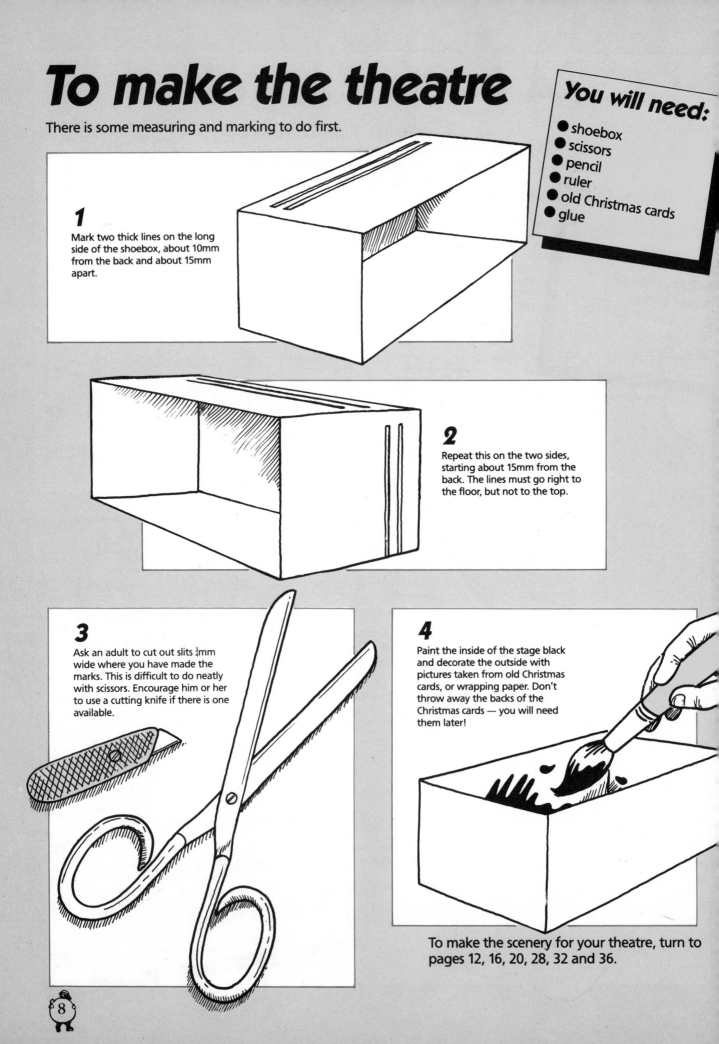

Christmas word game

How many words can you make from the letters of the word 'Christmas'? Each word must have at least three letters, and you can use each letter only once. (Don't forget to use the second 's' to make the plural wherever this is possible!) Answers on page 48.

Your score

20 or over	Good
40 or over	Excellent
79	Better than the author!

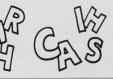

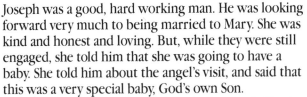

Joseph's Dream

Joseph was a good, hard working man. He was looking forward very much to being married to Mary. She was kind and honest and loving. But, while they were still engaged, she told him that she was going to have a baby. She told him about the angel's visit, and said that this was a very special baby, God's own Son.

But Joseph was shocked. It was hard to believe Mary's story. How could he marry her now? What would people say?

Joseph was a kind man. He didn't want Mary to be disgraced. So he planned to break off the engagement quietly.

That night, an angel appeared to Joseph in a dream.

'Don't be afraid to marry Mary,' he said. 'What she says is true. She is going to have a baby who is God's own Son, and you will call him Jesus, because he will save his people from their sins.'

Now Joseph knew for certain that Mary had told the truth. And God had chosen him – an ordinary village carpenter – to look after that special baby, Jesus.

Joseph loved Mary very much – and he was going to marry her.

9

Advent ring

If you don't want to hang up your Advent ring, you can make a table ring instead. Follow the instructions but take a slice off the bottom of the potatoes so they stand flat. Put the ring on an old cake board before you decorate it, and tie the ribbons in bows.

1

Ask an adult to snip the hook off the coat hanger and bend it into a circle.

2

Push the potatoes onto the circle of wire until it is completely covered.

3

Tie the ribbons round at equal intervals.

4

Push in the four candle holders well away from the ribbons and put in the candles.

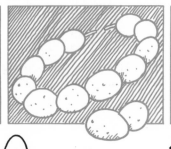
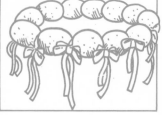

You will need:

- wire coat hanger
- small potatoes
- holly sprigs or evergreen twigs
- 4 lengths of ribbon
- card ring (draw round a plate for the size and cut out the middle)
- baubles
- hair pins
- candles and candle holders

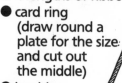

Take care — candles can be dangerous. For extra safety, spray the foliage with water before the candles are lit and always ask an adult to help you light them. Do not leave candles burning unattended.

5

Use the hook to make holes in the potatoes and then push in the holly or sprigs of evergreen.

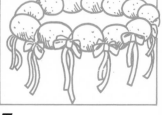

6

Put the potato ring upside-down on a table while you attach each ribbon to the circle of card, and then hang it up.

7

Continue to push the holly into the potatoes and add some baubles, using hair pins to secure them.

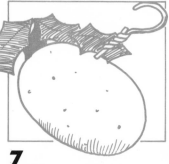

8

Light one candle each Sunday in Advent for an hour — perhaps while you have lunch — lighting all your candles on the last Sunday before Christmas Day.

Pot-pourri

A true pot-pourri is a mixture of special aromatic oils and petals, and the recipes can be complicated.

Here is a recipe using a variety of dried herbs and spices — a small pinch of each will be more than enough. Use some of these to make a fragrant sachet. Don't forget to ask before you raid the kitchen cupboards!

> thyme marjoram allspice dried lemon peel mint basil sage nutmeg cinnamon caraway seed rosemary whole cloves dried orange peel mace

Pot-pourri bag

A bag of sweet-smelling pot-pourri adds fragrance to wardrobes and may help keep moths away. It is a lovely gift to make and to receive.

You will need:

- material, such as pretty cotton 15cm×20cm
- ribbon
- needle and thread
- lace 20cm (optional)
- cotton wool
- pot-pourri

1

Fold a small hem along one long end of the material and stitch the lace on. Fold it in half, right sides together, and stitch along the bottom and up the side. Turn the right way out.

2

Fold the ribbon in half and stitch it to one side, about 3 or 4cm down.

3

Make a square of cotton wool and put some pot-pourri in the middle. Put a second square on top.

4

Put the cotton wool 'sandwich' into the little bag and tie the ribbon tightly.

Ring tree

If you know someone who can never remember where she has put her rings, why not make this ring tree to keep them in one place?

You will need:

- toilet roll middle
- cotton wool or rolled-up tissues
- square of soft fabric approximately 25cm²
- pinking shears
- rubber band
- glue
- braid

1

Hold a tape measure around one end of the tube and mark around the top in centimetres.

2

Cut down into the tube with the pinking shears where you have made the marks. Cut to the same depth each time.

3

Paint the tube inside and allow to dry.

4

Paint the tube outside and allow to dry.

5

Place the cotton wool or tissues in the middle of the square of fabric. Gather the fabric up and twist, securing with a rubber band.

6

Gently push the stuffing up into the tube until it is about two thirds of the way up. Tuck in the ends of the fabric. If it won't stay in place, add a little more stuffing until it is held firmly.

7

Glue braid around the base to decorate your ring tree.

8

Carefully bend alternate prongs outwards. Rings should now balance on them!

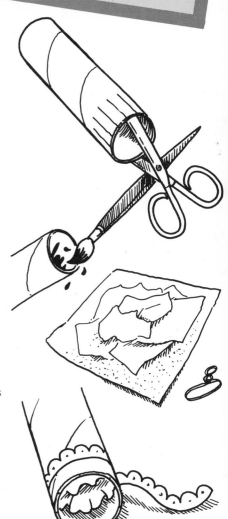

To make the scenery for your puppet theater

1

The permanent backdrop for the theater can be painted onto a sheet of paper and glued into the back of the box. Measure the correct size by putting the box on top of the paper and drawing around it. Cut the paper just inside the line, and it should fit. The backdrop needs to have hills, road and trees. Copy the picture on page 32 on to the paper and color brightly.
Glue on sequins or glitter for stars in the night sky.

2

To make the scenery you will need 3 sheets of stiff card. The card needs to be $\frac{1}{2}$ in. shorter than the length of the slit on the top of the box, and 1$\frac{1}{2}$ in. longer than the height of the box.

The first card has Mary's room on one side and the inn on the other.

The second card has the room with the manger on one side with a window for the animals to look out of. This is a half-sized card.

The third card has King Herod's palace on one side and is blank on the other.

You will find outlines of these to trace or copy on pages 16, 20, 28, 32 and 36. Color each piece of scenery brightly, adding extras where you can. Use glitter for stars or cut out star shapes from pieces of foil.

3

The room where the animals are kept needs a window. Cut out the quarter circle shown and look for the heads of horses, donkeys or cows on old Christmas cards. Glue these onto the back of the card so the animals look through the window.

4

Use the small space at the top of each piece of scenery to write on which it is.

Mary visits Elizabeth

After the angel had spoken to Mary, she decided to visit her cousin Elizabeth. She wanted to share her good news, and to see if the angel's message about Elizabeth was true.

Yes! Elizabeth and Zechariah were expecting a baby. After all these years of waiting, now that they were old, God had promised them a baby boy. He would be called John and he would be part of God's plan, telling people about God's promised Saviour – Jesus.

As soon as Mary arrived, Elizabeth *knew*. Mary didn't even have to tell her what had happened. Elizabeth's baby jumped for joy inside her, and she found the words tumbling out:

'What wonderful news!' she said. 'You are to be the mother of God's own Son – the Saviour who has been promised to us.'

Suddenly Mary was full of happiness. She sang a song of praise to God, for at long last God's promises to his people were coming true. Mary stayed with Elizabeth for three months. Then she returned to Nazareth to be married.

Pebble People

If you collect pebbles when you're by the sea but never know what to do with them, here is one idea to transform them into a super gift.

1
Cover one of the larger pebbles with a layer of hardening clay.

2
Dip the base of each of the other pebbles in glue and press firmly into the clay so they stand upright and form a group. Leave to dry.

3
Onto each pebble paint two white ovals for eyes and allow to dry. Complete the face by painting on two black circles within the ovals and a mouth below them. Allow to dry.

4
Dab some glue onto the head of the tallest pebble and dip it into some granules to make the hair.

5
When everything is completely dry, apply a coat of varnish to highlight the colours in the pebbles.

You will need:

- small flat pebbles (various colours if possible)
- acrylic paint (black and white)
- glue
- modelling clay
- varnish
- coloured chippings, glitter or sugar

Recipe cards

This is a useful gift for a keen cook. The cards are decorated but left blank so that favourite recipes can be added.

1
Make a thin band out of the paper to hold the postcards, using glue to keep it together. Write 'Recipe Cards' on the band.

2
Divide the cards into 8 groups. Decide what illustration you want for each kind of recipe.

3
Use the same corner of each card to draw on your illustration. Keep it small but colourful.

You will need:

- pack of blank postcards
- colouring pencils or felt-tip pens
- paper and glue

POULTRY
VEGETABLES
PASTA
CHEESE
MEAT
FISH
EGGS
FRUIT

Pine-cone Santa

You will need:
- cotton wool
- glue
- 2 pine cones
- white felt
- blue marker
- red felt
- cord
- pipe-cleaner

This pine-cone Santa is ideal for a window sill decoration, or to hang on the Christmas tree.

1

Spread glue over the pointed ends of both cones and jam one cone on top of the other at a slight angle. Wiggle the cones around until they will stand upright. Leave to dry.

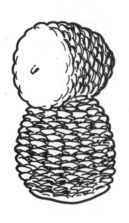

Did you know...

Santa Claus is just one of the names given to the person who is supposed to bring gifts at Christmas.

This name comes from the Dutch name for St Nicholas, Sinta Class. We don't know many facts about St Nicholas except that he was bishop of Myra, in Asia Minor, during the fourth century.

One legend says that Nicholas secretly saved a very poor family from starvation by dropping three bags of gold in at a window on separate visits. He was discovered on the last occasion by the father of the family, but Nicholas swore him to secrecy.

In Holland, St Nicholas traditionally rides a white horse, but in Sweden he is drawn by mountain goats. No one really knows how he came to have a pack of reindeer!

2

Cut a quarter circle of red felt, glue the straight edges and roll into a cone for Santa's hat. Use a paper clip to keep the edges together until the glue is dry. Dab a little glue on the tip of the hat and add a tiny ball of cotton wool.

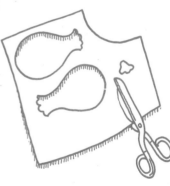

3

Using the red felt again, cut out two sack shapes and glue them together. Leave to dry. Tie thin cord around the neck to make Santa's sack.

4

Cut out two circles of white felt and mark two eyes with the blue marker pen. Cut out a nose from the red felt.

5

To make your Santa, wind a pipe-cleaner around the lower cone and twist it around the neck of the sack. Glue the eyes and nose onto the base of the top cone and glue on the hat. Finally, ease a little cotton wool into a beard shape and glue onto Santa's face.

Journey to Bethlehem

In those days, the Roman Emperor, Augustus, made all the people return to their home towns to register. Joseph came from Bethlehem, King David's city, because he belonged to the family-line of David.

So Mary and Joseph set off for Bethlehem from Nazareth. It was a long, long journey on rough and dusty roads. Everybody was on the move and the roads were crowded and busy.

Mary was very tired. The baby was due soon and she desperately wanted to lie down and rest. But, when they arrived in Bethlehem, it was the same story everywhere – no room!

All the guest-rooms were taken. The inn was full already. But someone made space at last. Mary and Joseph had to share the room with the animals, but it was somewhere to rest, and there was soft straw to sleep on.

Pictures make lovely gifts for both friends and family. Here are several ideas you can adapt according to your skill and imagination.

Make a picture

1

Place the larger piece of card in the middle of the fabric. Hold it in place with sticky tape.

2

Cut the corners off the fabric.

3

Fold the edges over the card and tape lightly.

4

Using the needle and thread, sew across from one side to the other and pull the stitches tight. Put small stitches across the corners so the card is kept firmly in place.

You will need:

For the mount

- piece of fabric approximately 15cm×12cm
- sticky tape
- 1 piece of card 13cm×10cm
- 1 piece of card 12cm×9cm
- needle and thread

5

Sew a loop of ribbon onto the fabric.

6

Glue the second square of card over the back to cover the stitches. Press firmly in place and allow to dry. Turn the mount over so the fabric is facing you.

Now that you have made your mount, use these ideas to make your picture.

Mirror picture

1

Decide what picture you want on your mirror and make a sketch on some paper.

2

Using a felt-tip pen draw the outline of your sketch onto the mirror.

3

Carefully fill one section at a time with glue and sprinkle on the coloured granules, gradually building up the picture. Wipe off excess glue with a cotton wool bud. Be sure to let each part dry before you continue with the next.

4

When the picture is finished, apply a light coat of varnish over the granules only. Press the adhesive tab on the back.

You will need:

- a mirror
- self-adhesive tab
- coloured crystals or granules such as sugar or caraway seeds
- glue

Picture using dried leaves, flowers or grasses

1

Arrange the dried leaves and flowers on a sheet of thick card. Glue each part firmly in place.

2

When completely dry, glue the card onto the mount.

Painted picture

1

Take a piece of thick card about 2cm smaller all around than your mount. Cover the card with paper, tucking the edges behind as before, but using glue to keep it in place.

2

Paint a picture on the front and allow paint to dry. Glue your picture to the mount.

Seaside theme

1

Decide what your seaside picture will look like by sketching it on paper first.

2

Use small assorted shells to represent sailing boats or rocks on the shore, and blue embroidery thread for the sea. A piece of some old fishnet tights or an old net curtain could represent a fisherman's net.

3

Glue items to the card and press down firmly. Allow to dry. Glue the finished seaside picture onto the mount.

3-dimensional pictures

You will need:

- 3 identical pictures
- thin cork tile — or thick card
- glue
- sharp scissors
- stiff card for backing sheet
- self-adhesive tab
- a calendar (optional)

1

Paste one of the pictures onto the sheet of stiff card. This is the 'base picture'.

2

Cut out from the second and third pictures the areas you want to build up — for example, the dog, the dress, the shoes, the hat. This will give you two sets of cut-outs and one pasted-down picture.

3

Place small squares of cork or thick card on the base picture on those areas you want to make 3-dimensional.

4

Take the first set of cut-outs and glue them on top of these squares. When this is dry, glue a second layer of cork or card squares in place and then the second layer of cut-outs. Your picture is now complete!

5

Press the self-adhesive tab on the back and a calendar on the bottom if wished.

Celebrate Christmas

Where do you think these people celebrate Christmas? Their hats give you the clue. Answers on page 48.

1
2
3
4
5
6

The king is born!

While Mary and Joseph were staying in Bethlehem, the time came for the baby to be born.

It was night-time when Mary first held the baby Jesus in her arms. She and Joseph were so happy; they looked in wonder at this little baby – so small, so defenceless, yet God's own Son! Here was the Saviour, the King that the people of God had been waiting for. This was the Prince of Peace that the prophets had talked about many years before. It was wonderful!

Mary wrapped the baby in strips of cloth, as the custom was, and laid him in the manger to sleep.

Pirate pencils

With a little time and trouble, you can make a pencil into a special gift for a friend.

1

Cut the felt to the size and shape shown here.

2

Stitch the hat together, leaving the bottom edge open. Sew the gold sequin onto one edge as an ear-ring. Glue the two white strips of felt on as cross bones.

3

Either glue the bead onto the pencil and allow to dry, or make a round shape out of the clay, push in the pencil and allow to dry. Glue the piece of fabric just below the bead, winding it around and around until it is completely used.

4

Glue the hat to the top of the bead, and the beard to the bottom.

5

Mark on one eye with a felt-tip pen or paint.

6

Glue the black sequin on as an eyepatch and use a felt-tip pen to mark the strings.

Using this method, you can make Santa pencils, cat pencils, or anything else you think your friends would like.

decorations

1

Staple the ribbon to the card at one end. Wind ribbon carefully round the card and staple the other end.

2

Bend the strip of card into a circle and staple the ends together.

3

Tie the cord around the card leaving a hanging loop at the top and knot firmly. Thread beads on to the loose ends.

4

Tie green tinsel around the top to add sparkle.

To make heart shapes

At stage 2, put the outside edges of the card together and staple. Pinch the bottom edges together and staple. Continue as before.

Did you know...

Mary laid Jesus in a manger because there was no room in the inn. In those days animals were often kept in a room attached to the house. A manger was the trough where the animals fed and may have been cut out of stone.

Which one?

What gifts did the children receive at Christmas? Can you work it out? Answers on page 48.

Mark

Katie

Graham

Sarah

Emily

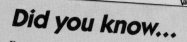

Did you know...

People have been sending Christmas cards to each other only since the middle of the last century.

The first known card was designed by John Horsley in 1843 and was the idea of Sir Henry Cole, a civil servant concerned with Post Office reform.

Few people could afford to buy and send cards at first because printing and postal rates were so expensive. But by 1900, cards were being made cheaply all over Europe.

Christmas cards

You will need:

- large sheet of thick paper or card
- colouring pencils or
- felt-tip pens
- glue
- ribbon
- darning needle
- scissors
- coloured paper

Cards that are designed and made by hand have a special charm — some of which comes from knowing that time and thought have gone into the making.

Here are a few ideas to start you off: the pictures you make will probably reflect the weather you have (or would like to have!) at Christmas.

1

Decide how big you want your cards to be. Draw lines across the paper using a ruler and carefully cut along them.

2

Take each strip and mark into suitable widths. Cut along the lines you have drawn. Fold each card in half.

3

Write a greeting on the inside, and on the back 'Designed and made by.....'

4

Open out the card so that the front and back are facing you.

1

Cut one side of white paper with ordinary scissors, the other with pinking shears. Glue on to green backing card. Mark tree trunks on with black felt-tip, and the ice with silver felt-tip.

2

Cut three tree shapes out of green card and glue on to a white background. Spread a thin layer of glue over the trees and sprinkle blue glitter on one, silver on the second and red on the third. Use a red felt-tip to draw on tubs for the trees.

3

Draw a picture of sea and sand on to a white background. Use a brown felt-tip pen for the tree trunk and glue on short lengths of green tinsel for the leaves. Some of your designs can be graphic or artistic.

4

Choose one or two verses from the Bible that tell part of the Christmas story and write them in a spiral using different coloured pens.

Stained glass Christmas cards

You will need:

- black card
- white card
- scissors
- glue
- clear cellophane (assorted colours) or tissue paper
- greaseproof paper
- felt-tip pens

Here are two ways of making your Christmas cards look extra special. The important thing is to let the light shine through the 'stained glass' so that you get the best effect.

Method 1

1

Cut out pieces of card 20cm by 30cm and fold in half.

2

Turn to the pages of tracing paper and colour each of the pictures with bright felt-tip pens.

3

If you want to make more than 6 cards, use these as templates and trace the pictures using the greaseproof paper.

4

Cut around the outer bold lines so that you have a selection of 'stained glass' windows.

5

Take a piece of folded card and cut out the same shape as one of the stained glass windows but using the inside bold line for the size.

6

Glue between the two bold lines and carefully stick on the inside of the card where you have made the cut-out, so that the right side shows through the window.

7

Write your message on the lower half of the inside page. Try the card out on a window ledge by opening it out and letting the light shine through.

Method 2

1

Cut out pieces of black card 20cm by 30cm and fold in half.

2

Sketch a simple design on paper and then transfer it onto the front of the card. Keep the shapes large to make the cutting out easy.

3

Holding the two folds of card together, cut out between the 'frame' so that you go through two thicknesses to the back. You will be left with a skeleton effect on the front and back of the card.

4

Cut out pieces of coloured cellophane or tissue paper using the pieces of black cut-out card as templates but allowing a little extra all around.

5

Dab glue on the back of the black frame and stick the cellophane or tissue paper over the matching hole.

6

Close card to check there are no gaps, and then open up and glue the black frame on the inside back of the card. Press together firmly and leave under a heavy book until dry.

7

Write your greeting on a piece of white or coloured paper and stick this on the back of your window card.

Bouquet garni

If there are keen cooks among your friends or family, they will love to have these small bags of herbs made up ready to add to casseroles.

You will need:

- muslin — cut into circles 20cm in diameter
- dried herbs — thyme, parsley, sage, onion flakes, basil, oregano
- celery salt
- thread
- thin ribbon

Christmas dessert

'Star Special' — a dessert that will look really good, but is very easy to make.

You will need:

- ice cream
- sparklers
- wafers
- fruit — soft fresh fruit or tinned
- jelly (any colours)
- whipped cream (an aerosol can is good for this)
- long glasses or
- short sundae dishes

1

Cut the fruit into small pieces and put some at the bottom of each glass, saving some for later.

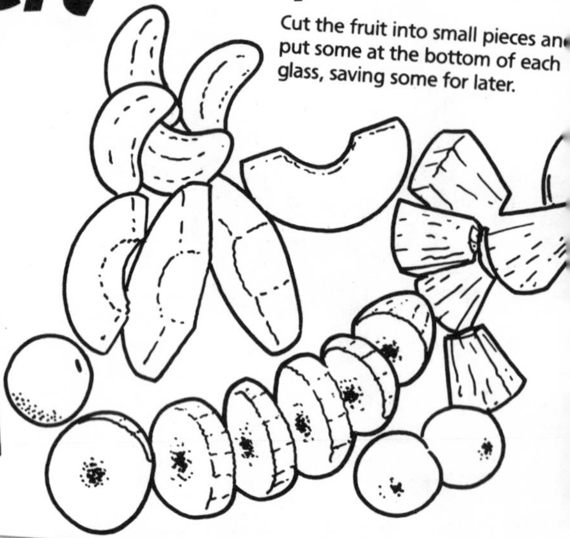

Muddled meals

Christmas dinner is a traditional meal — but can you work out what everyone has on their plates? It seems to have got muddled! Answers on page 48.

- nerrybarc ceasu ———————
- yardnb tubret ———————
- holacatips ———————
- micenipes ———————
- okpr ———————
- elbssurs ———————

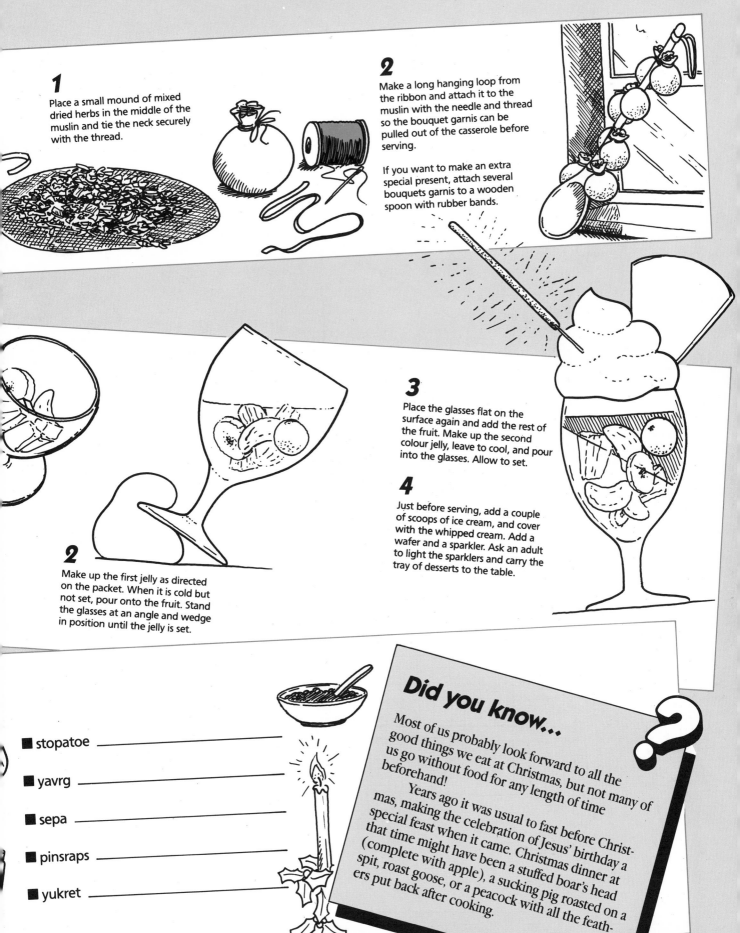

1

Place a small mound of mixed dried herbs in the middle of the muslin and tie the neck securely with the thread.

2

Make a long hanging loop from the ribbon and attach it to the muslin with the needle and thread so the bouquet garnis can be pulled out of the casserole before serving.

If you want to make an extra special present, attach several bouquets garnis to a wooden spoon with rubber bands.

3

Place the glasses flat on the surface again and add the rest of the fruit. Make up the second colour jelly, leave to cool, and pour into the glasses. Allow to set.

4

Just before serving, add a couple of scoops of ice cream, and cover with the whipped cream. Add a wafer and a sparkler. Ask an adult to light the sparklers and carry the tray of desserts to the table.

2

Make up the first jelly as directed on the packet. When it is cold but not set, pour onto the fruit. Stand the glasses at an angle and wedge in position until the jelly is set.

■ stopatoe _____

■ yavrg _____

■ sepa _____

■ pinsraps _____

■ yukret _____

Did you know...

Most of us probably look forward to all the good things we eat at Christmas, but not many of us go without food for any length of time beforehand!

Years ago it was usual to fast before Christmas, making the celebration of Jesus' birthday a special feast when it came. Christmas dinner at that time might have been a stuffed boar's head (complete with apple), a sucking pig roasted on a spit, roast goose, or a peacock with all the feathers put back after cooking.

Gift-wrapped

Can you guess what is in each of these parcels?

Answers on page 48.

The shepherds' surprise

In the town of Bethlehem, everyone was asleep – except for Mary and Joseph. But, out on the hillside around the town, some shepherds were looking after their sheep.

The shepherds were just ordinary people – but this was no ordinary night. They sat huddled in their cloaks as usual, talking and keeping watch over their flocks. Suddenly the whole sky was filled with light, and one of God's angels appeared to them.

The shepherds were terrified. They hid their eyes and huddled closer together. What was going on?

'Don't be afraid,' said the angel. 'I have come to give you good news, good news for the whole world. Today, in David's city, your Saviour has been born, Christ the Lord. And this is how you will recognize him – you will find a baby wrapped in cloth and lying in a manger.'

As if that wasn't enough, the whole sky was suddenly full of bright angels, a great host of God's messengers, singing:

'Glory to God in the highest,
and peace to people on earth.'

Then the angels were gone. And the shepherds set out for Bethlehem, to find the baby.

29

A Christmas Game

How many things can you get inside a matchbox? Divide your friends or family into teams, and give a time limit of ten minutes.

The rules are simple. You are allowed only one item per type of thing: in other words, you can't fill it with 1,000 pine needles!

Here are a few ideas to start you off:

tree decoration	leaf
raisin	petal
sultana	twig
cracker label	pebble
cake decoration	staple
holly berry	nail
pine needle	screw
Christmas stamp	rawlplug
piece of ribbon	
gift tag	
pea	
bean	
rice grain, long and short	
lentil	
hair clip	
paper clip	
pinch of salt	
peppercorn	
pinch of spice	
pin	

Allow 5 points for each Christmas item, and 1 point for anything else.

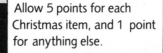

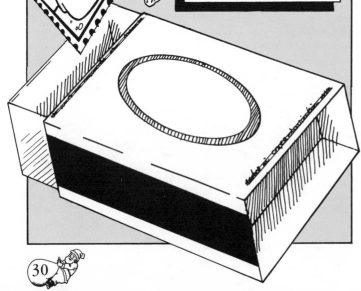

Year Star

One of the many enjoyable things about decorating the Christmas tree each year is bringing out the decorations from their wrappings and remembering where they were bought, or who gave them to us, or what we were like when we made them.

Here is an idea you might like to share. Each Christmas a Year Star is made by a member of the family, and hung on the tree. You will find that the collection steadily grows, and will decorate your tree in a unique and personal way that is special to your family.

You will need:

- paint
- glitter
- scissors
- hole punch
- thread
- large sheet of thick paper or card
- sequins or beads
- old Christmas cards

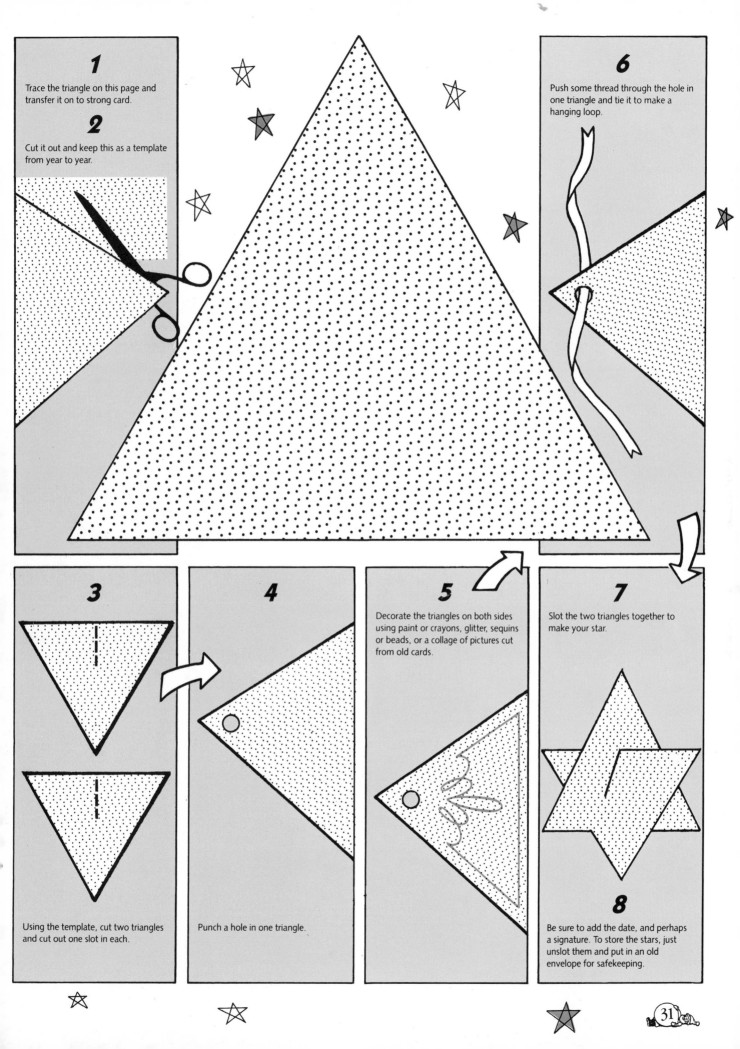

1

Trace the triangle on this page and transfer it on to strong card.

2

Cut it out and keep this as a template from year to year.

3

Using the template, cut two triangles and cut out one slot in each.

4

Punch a hole in one triangle.

5

Decorate the triangles on both sides using paint or crayons, glitter, sequins or beads, or a collage of pictures cut from old cards.

6

Push some thread through the hole in one triangle and tie it to make a hanging loop.

7

Slot the two triangles together to make your star.

8

Be sure to add the date, and perhaps a signature. To store the stars, just unslot them and put in an old envelope for safekeeping.

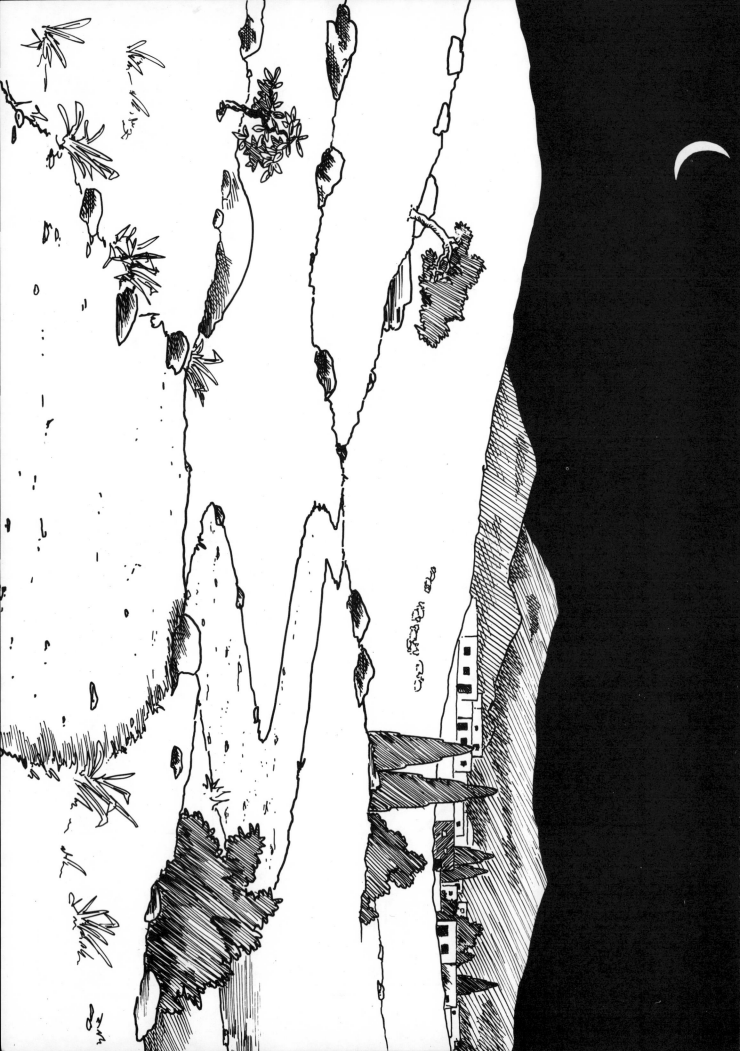

The shepherds find the baby

The shepherds hurried to Bethlehem. There was no time to lose! As they ran they talked excitedly to each other about what they had seen and heard. It was almost like a dream – except that they knew they weren't dreaming.

Before long, they were gazing in wonder at the tiny baby, sleeping in the manger. So – it was true! They told Mary and Joseph what the angel had said to them, and about the huge crowd of angels singing God's praises. Mary listened carefully to all these things. She would always remember them.

The shepherds returned to their sheep, singing and full of joy. Everyone was amazed to hear their story about the angels. Could it really be true? God's promised Saviour – asleep in a manger?

Make a soft toy

Here is a gift that has two different uses. If you live somewhere cold and need to keep in the warmth, it makes a smashing draught excluder. If not, it makes a lovely soft toy!

You will need:
- tube of card, rolled-up newspapers or clean, laddered tights
- ribbon or string
- trimming and fabric of choice

1

Cut the legs off the tights. Pull one leg over the cardboard or newspaper tube and knot the end.

2

Pull the second leg on the other way around so the knots do not build up at one end.

3

Keep on adding tights until you have built up a soft covering layer.

For the caterpillar, cover the roll with the legs of some old green tights or green fabric. Tie wool tightly around the body at intervals to make the segments. Add a fringe for the legs. Glue on eyes and a mouth and pipe-cleaners with cotton wool on the top to make antennae.

For the snake, either buy some printed cotton with a snakeskin design on it, or paint a pattern on some plain white cotton with fabric paint. Cut out the fabric in a shape to cover your tube and fold over with the right side inside. Machine-stitch the long seam and one end. Turn the fabric the right way out and pull the snakeskin covering over the tube. Glue on two felt eyes and a red felt forked tongue. Finish it off by stitching the open end by hand, folding the raw end in as you stitch.

For the dog, cover the tube with dark coloured fabric, using the instructions for the snake. Glue on felt ears, eyes, paws and tail.

For the Christmas cracker, take a piece of pretty fabric twice the diameter of the tube and slightly longer. Hem the edges. Cover the tube and tie the ends with ribbon, so it looks like a cracker. Leave one fairly long loop of ribbon so the draught excluder can be hung onto the door handle.

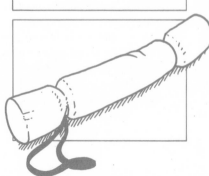

Did you know...

Although we know that Jesus was born when the Roman Emperor Augustus ruled the world, we do not know the exact day or month. The early Christians wanted to celebrate the birth of Jesus: they chose mid-winter not only because it was a time when people needed to be cheered up by celebrations and feasting, but because other festivals, such as the Roman festival of Saturnalia, were held around this time. Christians decided to keep the same holiday but give it new meaning, reminding themselves that with Jesus, God's light had come into the world.
Today Christians in some parts of the world celebrate his birthday on 6 January and others on 25 December.

Christmas tree pompoms

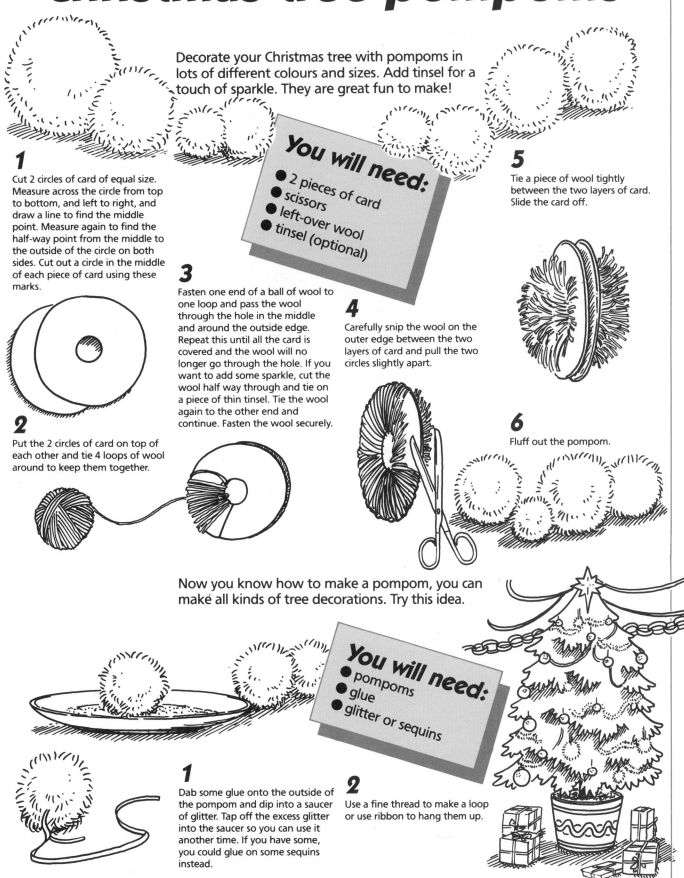

Decorate your Christmas tree with pompoms in lots of different colours and sizes. Add tinsel for a touch of sparkle. They are great fun to make!

You will need:
- 2 pieces of card
- scissors
- left-over wool
- tinsel (optional)

1
Cut 2 circles of card of equal size. Measure across the circle from top to bottom, and left to right, and draw a line to find the middle point. Measure again to find the half-way point from the middle to the outside of the circle on both sides. Cut out a circle in the middle of each piece of card using these marks.

2
Put the 2 circles of card on top of each other and tie 4 loops of wool around to keep them together.

3
Fasten one end of a ball of wool to one loop and pass the wool through the hole in the middle and around the outside edge. Repeat this until all the card is covered and the wool will no longer go through the hole. If you want to add some sparkle, cut the wool half way through and tie on a piece of thin tinsel. Tie the wool again to the other end and continue. Fasten the wool securely.

4
Carefully snip the wool on the outer edge between the two layers of card and pull the two circles slightly apart.

5
Tie a piece of wool tightly between the two layers of card. Slide the card off.

6
Fluff out the pompom.

Now you know how to make a pompom, you can make all kinds of tree decorations. Try this idea.

You will need:
- pompoms
- glue
- glitter or sequins

1
Dab some glue onto the outside of the pompom and dip into a saucer of glitter. Tap off the excess glitter into the saucer so you can use it another time. If you have some, you could glue on some sequins instead.

2
Use a fine thread to make a loop or use ribbon to hang them up.

35

Wise men from the East

At the time when Jesus was born in Bethlehem, some wise men far away in the East prepared for a long journey.

These wise men studied the movements of the planets and the stars in the sky. A bright new star had appeared – a special star, which told them that an important person – a king – had been born.

They set off, following the star, and travelled many miles until they came to Jerusalem, the capital city. They went straight to the palace, for they felt sure that this was the place for a royal prince to be born.

'Where is the baby born to be king of the Jews?' they asked. 'We have seen his star, and we have come to worship him.'

Monkey mobile

This troupe of monkeys makes an ideal gift for younger brothers or sisters.

1

Trace the monkey from this page and transfer to a piece of card.

2

Cut around this outline then use it as a template to cut out as many monkeys as you want in your mobile.

3

Colour them with your paints or felt-tip pens, and decorate with sequins or glitter.

4

Tie the twine around the arm of one monkey and hang it up. Hook on all the monkeys below. Make banana cut-outs in the same way and add bunches of bananas to balance.

Ostrich marionette

This string puppet makes a great gift for a friend — but you'll probably find a lot of adults playing with it too!

You will need:

- cotton reel
- small wedge of wood
- 2 small circles of wood or large buttons
- wool in two colours or coloured cotton wool balls
- stapler
- glue
- lolly sticks
- twine or thick cotton
- felt-tip pens
- cotton reel

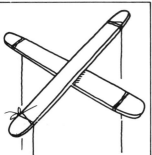

1

Staple, tack or glue the sticks into a cross shape.

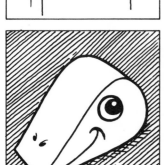

2

Draw the eyes and beak on each side of the wedge of wood to make the head.

3

Make 4 pompoms from the coloured wool. (See page 35.) Using the first colour, make two 5cm in diameter and one 6cm. Make the last pompom from the second colour 3cm in diameter.

4

Thread 30cm of wool through the cotton reel and staple or glue in place. Staple the wool onto the small wooden circles, or glue on to the buttons to make the feet.

5

Cut a piece of wool 10cm in length. Staple or glue one end to the underside of the cotton reel and staple the other end to the wedge of wood.

6

Glue the smallest pompom on the back of the wedge, one medium-sized pompom onto each side of the cotton reel, and the largest one on the back of the cotton reel.

7

Cut three equal lengths of twine and fix on to the top of the head and to the knee joints. Cut one shorter length and staple it to the top of the cotton reel.

8

Adjust for length and tie the twine to the crossbars. You can now make your ostrich move about by moving the crossbars.

Puppet theater props

The palm tree

1

Roll the sheet of paper into a tight tube and tape it in two places.

2

With sharp scissors, cut down into the tube at ⅛ in. intervals until you have cut all the way around.

3

Open out the 'branches.' Lightly dab the ends with glue and sprinkle on some green glitter.

4

Tape the palm tree to one side of the stage.

The gifts

Gold Paint a playbrick or matchbox with gold paint, or cover with gold colored foil.

Frankincense Paint the top of a liquid detergent bottle and cover with sequins to make an exotic jar.

Myrrh Turn your jar lid upside-down and glue the inside. Fill with beads and allow to dry.

Sheep Cut an oval of card. Tease a ball of cotton wool into the shape of a sleeping sheep and glue onto the card base. Mark ears and eyes on with a black felt-tip pen. Make two or three sheep and one or two smaller ones to represent lambs.

The star

1

Cut a rectangle out of the stiff card and copy onto it the lines in the diagram.

2

Cut away the shaded areas. Dab some glue on to the remaining card and sprinkle the glitter all over.

3

Tape or glue the star to the other side of the stage.

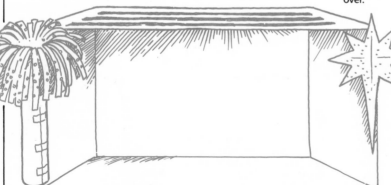

King Herod

Before long, King Herod himself heard about the wise men from the East.

'A baby king!' he thundered angrily. 'Not in my palace!' Then he began to get worried. What did it mean? He was the king, and he didn't want any rivals.

Herod called together all the chief priests and teachers of the law. They would know the answer.

'Where do the prophets say this baby king will be born?' he demanded.

'In Bethlehem,' they told him, for that was what God had promised.

So Herod called the wise men from the East to a secret meeting in the palace. He had an evil plan in mind, but he kept that to himself. He asked them to tell him all about the star and when it had appeared. Then he told them to go to Bethlehem, saying, 'When you find this baby king, send me word, so that I may go and pay my respects.'

And so the wise men set off for Bethlehem.

Table decoration

You will need:

- one third of a toilet roll tube
- tinsel
- pipe cleaner
- shiny bead
- glue
- glitter
- silver paint
- stiff shiny card

To make the name holder

1

Cut one third of a toilet roll tube as shown and paint it silver or any colour of your choice.

2

Cut out squares of card large enough to fit into the slot in the tube. Fold in half and write a name on each one so that every member of the family has one. Perhaps some friends will be joining you for Christmas. Do a card for them too!

3

Slot the name card into the slits in the painted tube.

To make the flower decoration

1

Thread the pipe-cleaner through the bead so that it just peeps through, and use a thick, setting glue to hold it in place. Sprinkle glitter onto the glue to disguise it.

2

Knot about 3cm of tinsel around the base of the bead, leaving the ends free.

3

Cut out the flower shape from the stiff card.

4

Thread the pipe-cleaner and bead through the middle of the flower and put a small twist in the pipe cleaner on the right side to hold it up.

To combine the two parts

Balance the flower inside the name-holder tube, coiling the pipe-cleaner around inside. Put your table decorations on one side and keep until Christmas.

Christmas napkin rings

Instead of folding the napkins in a special way, these napkin rings can be your contribution to making the Christmas table look really festive.

1

Measure the length of the toilet roll and divide it into 3 sections. Mark the lines.

You will need:

- toilet roll tubes
- tin foil
- fine point scissors
- decorations as available
- glue
- tape measure

2

Cut the tube carefully along the lines so that the edge remains neat and straight.

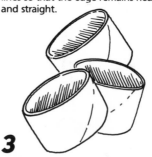

3

Cut a piece of foil large enough to cover each small tube. For the length, measure around the tube and add 4cm. For the width, measure the depth of the tube and double it. Roll the foil around the tube and tuck both ends in.

4

Keep turning the tube and smoothing the foil until you are satisfied with the result.

5

Here are some suggestions for decorating your napkin rings, but you will have other ideas of your own.
Glue on a small silk flower.
Cut a length of sequin braid and glue on.
Cut out a tiny Christmas tree from coloured foil and glue on.

Christmas boats

The Christmas table can be made to look attractive with decorations and with taking a little more care than usual over things like folding the napkins. You might like to try some of these ideas. Paper napkins, or starched linen napkins give the best results.

1

Fold the napkin in half from corner to corner, and in half again to give a crease down the middle.

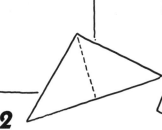

2

Fold the sides across to this crease.

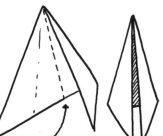

3

Turn it over and fold the 2 ends back. Fold in half lengthways.

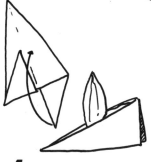

4

Stand the 'boat' up. If you are careful, you can lift out the top corner of the napkin to form a 'sail'!

Water-lilies

1

Fold each corner of the napkin into the middle.

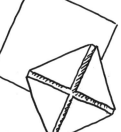

2

Turn the whole napkin over and repeat, folding the corners into the middle. You may need to press it at this stage.

3

Gently lift the corners out from underneath until it lies flat.

If all else fails, try these!

1

Roll up napkin from one corner.

2

Fold in half and tuck into a glass!

The Christingle

Christingle services are held in many churches on the Sunday before Christmas.

1

Make a candle-shaped hole in the middle of the orange.

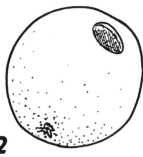

2

Fasten the red ribbon around the outside with a drawing pin.

3

Push the candle firmly into the hole in the orange, making sure it is kept upright.

4

Thread the fruit and nuts onto the cocktail sticks and push them into the orange.

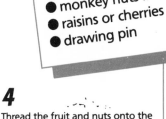

You will need:

- an orange
- a candle
- red ribbon
- 4 cocktail sticks
- monkey nuts in shells
- raisins or cherries
- drawing pin

Did you know...

The word Christingle means Christ-light. The Christingle service is a celebration of the coming of Jesus, the light of the world.

Children make a small fabric purse and put some money in it, and exchange it at the service for a Christingle. The money collected is used to help families with special needs.

The orange with its fruit and nuts represents the world, the four seasons and the fruits of the earth. The candle represents Jesus, who came to bring light to the world, while the red band stands for his blood, shed for us.

To make the characters

1

Turn to the centre pages of this book and gently push out each of the characters.

2

You now need 17 long pieces of stiff card so you can move your characters in and out of the theatre. Cut these out of an old washing powder box. (You could use florists' canes instead — the kind needed to support growing plants.)

3

Glue the card or cane to the back of each character along the base. Write the name of the character on the stick so you can identify them easily.

4

The characters can now be moved in and out of the slits at the side of your puppet theatre.

Did you know...

Only one person received presents at the first Christmas – the baby born to Mary and Joseph. Wise men, who knew that a king had been born, travelled to Bethlehem to worship him, bringing gifts of gold, frankincense and myrrh.

Each gift had a special meaning. It is thought that gold was given because it was a gift fit for a king. Frankincense is a sweet-smelling incense which reminds us that Jesus is God, and deserves to be loved and worshipped. Myrrh is a fragrant spice or ointment that was used to prepare dead bodies for burial, reminding us that Jesus was to give up his life to be the Saviour of the world.

Today, as we think of that first Christmas, we give presents to show that we love and care for each other. But St Paul tells us that Jesus himself was a gift – given by God the Father as a sign of his love for us.

Gifts for a baby king

The bright, shining star the wise men had seen in the East was now in front of them. They hurried on, eager to find the baby king.

When they got to Bethlehem, the star shone down on the place where Mary and Joseph were staying. It was just an ordinary house.

As soon as they saw Jesus, the wise men knelt down and worshipped him. At last they had found the one they had been looking for. A baby born to be a king.

They brought with them special gifts – gold, frankincense and myrrh. When they had given their gifts to Jesus, they left, going home a different way, because God warned them in a dream not to tell King Herod where the baby was.

Those wise men would never forget their long, long journey and the excitement and joy of seeing Jesus, the baby king.

This is only part of the story that the Bible tells us about Jesus' birth. You can find out more by reading the first two chapters of the Gospels of Matthew and Luke in the New Testament.

A game to play

This board game is simple to make — but it should keep you and your family amused for hours!

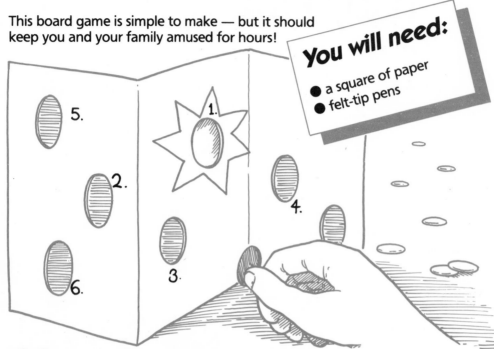

To make the board

Make some holes in a large sheet of card and number them. Cut a star-shaped hole near the centre. Make two folds in the card so it will stand up.

Each player has 20 tokens (buttons, coins or matchsticks will do) and 2 counters. The aim of the game is to get rid of all your tokens.

To play, each player in turn attempts to flip a counter through one of the holes on the board. If it goes through, the player gives away the number of tokens marked beside that hole to any other player.

When a player has only a few tokens left, the exact number must be scored to get rid of the rest. For example, if you have 3 tokens left, you must go through the number 3 hole.

When a player gets rid of all his tokens, he then has a free turn to flip his counter through the star shape in the middle of the card. If he succeeds the game is won. If he fails, however, he risks another player giving him more tokens to keep him in the game!

Thank you cards

We all like to receive gifts at Christmas and these cards are a lovely way to say 'thank you'. They are great fun to make and have your own personal mark!

1

Make up some thick paint and dip your thumb or a fingertip into it.

2

On a spare piece of paper, blot off the paint until there is just enough left to make a sharp finger or thumbprint.

3

Make your print on the card and let it dry.

4

Use your imagination to transform the prints into whatever you can. Here are some ideas:

Christmas origami

If you haven't tried this before, you'll be surprised at how quickly you pick it up. It takes a bit of practice — but looks very impressive.

1
Take your square of paper and fold it in half, and then in half again. Turn the paper the other way round and repeat this.

2
Open out your piece of paper which should now be creased into 16 square.

3
Fold each of the four corners into the middle.

4
Turn the square over.

5
Fold the four corners into the middle.

6
Copy the lines from here onto these triangles.

7
Turn the square over and copy these lines onto the four boxes. Colour the middle yellow and the outside any colour you choose.

8
Fold in half so the boxes are on the outside. Wiggle a finger and a thumb from each hand into the two little pockets on each side and bring your fingers and thumbs together. The origami square will fold inwards to form a point.

When you open the flower one way you will see the bees. When you open it another — the butterflies!

Once you have made this, you can draw all kinds of different things in the triangles

Another idea
Turn this upside-down and put sweets in it — or put a bauble in each section to make a table decoration.

Tree puzzle

Use the clues below to fill in the spaces on the tree. When you have finished, rearrange the first letter of each answer to make a seasonal word.

Clues:

1. The first letter of those who appeared on the hillside.
2. The shepherds hurried .. Bethlehem.
3. No room here.
4. A mother's name.
5. Sing a girl's name?
6. To buy back.
7. The sky was full of angels, ... praises to God.
8. One of those who looks after sheep.
9. A cry of praise.

Did you know...

The tradition of the Christmas tree goes back as far as the seventh century.

A Christian monk called Boniface prevented the tribes of Germany from offering a human sacrifice to their god, Odin. The victim, who had been tied to an oak tree, was set free, and Boniface told the people about the love and mercy of God. He offered them a young fir tree, and he and his companions placed candles on it so that it shone out in the darkness.

Answers

Can you re-unite these pairs? (page 3)

Santa — sack
tree — star
parcel — bow
fireplace — logs
snowflake — footprints
card — envelope

Merry Christmas! (page 5)

Nadolig Llawen — Welsh
God Jul — Swedish
Joyeux Noël — French
Feliz Navidad — Spanish
Frohe Weihnachten — German
Buon Natale — Italian
Vrolyk Kerstfeest — Dutch
Nollag Shona Dhuit — Gaelic

Christmas word game (page 9)

3 letters

cam	ham	ram
rat	his	mat
cat	sir	hit
him	mat	tic
arm	sat	sit
hat	mar	

4 letters

hams	rams	arms
mats	cats	hits
rich	hats	chit
mass	miss	hiss
sham	mach	tsar
tics	shim	trim
star	mast	mist
hair	hath	mash
rats	sits	sari
this	harm	tram
stir	hart	

5 letters

trims	trams	stars
mists	stirs	hairs
trash	mirth	chits
charm	smart	chasm
chair	maths	harms
masts	shams	tsars
amiss	smash	marsh
shirt	harts	

6 letters

smarts	chasms	shirts
schism	Christ	charms
chairs		

Celebrate Christmas (page 21)

1	Coolie hat	China
2	Fez	Egypt
3	Desert head cloth	Ethiopia
4	Sombrero	Mexico
5	Stetson	Texas
6	Beret	France

Which one? (page 23)

Emily — tennis racquet
Katie — dummy
Sarah — roller skates
Graham — book
Mark — football

Muddled meals (page 26)

turkey	chipolatas
peas	parsnips
potatoes	cranberry sauce
pork	mince pies
gravy	brandy butter
brussels	

Gift-wrapped (page 28)

1	Alarm clock	7	Plane
2	Car	8	Roller skates
3	Teddy bear	9	Doll
4	Cricket bat	10	Guitar
5	Train	11	Football
6	Tennis racquet	12	Trumpet

Tree puzzle (page 47)

Angels — A	Singing — S
To — T	Shepherds — S
Inn — I	Halleluia — H
Mary — M	
Carol — C	Christmas
Redeem — R	

Copyright © 1985 Lion Publishing

Published by
Lion Publishing plc
Sandy Lane West, Littlemore, Oxford, England
ISBN 0 7459 1825 5
Albatross Books Pty Ltd
PO Box 320, Sutherland,
NSW 2232, Australia
ISBN 0 86760 638 X

First edition 1985
Reprinted 1986 (twice), 1988, 1989

Printed in Thailand